LEARNING TOGETHER

LET'S DO SUMS

This book belongs to ....

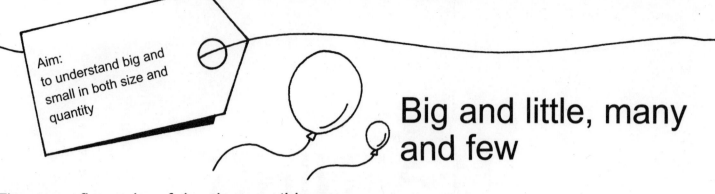

Aim:
to understand big and
small in both size and
quantity

Big and little, many and few

There are five pairs of drawings on this page.
Between each pair draw a green arrow from the bigger drawing to the smaller drawing.
Between two of the pairs draw a red arrow from the drawing containing more objects to the drawing containing fewer objects.

Count the animals

Aim:
to identify the numbers 1 to 5 in a series of five objects.

Colour the fifth bear, the second seal, the third dog and the first and fourth tortoise.

Aim:
to identify objects having
something in common.

Find the things that go together

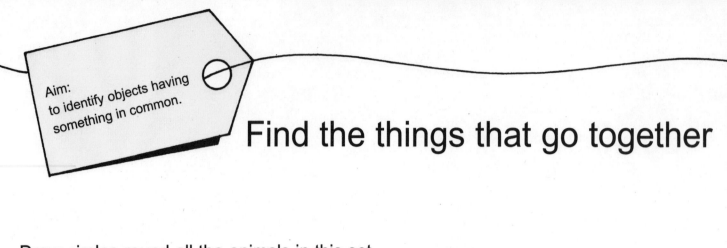

Draw circles round all the animals in this set.

Draw circles round all the things used for drinking in this set.

Draw circles round everything in this set that can fly.

Aim:
to count a quantity of objects and produce the same or different quantities of other objects.

As many as, more than, fewer than

How many boats are there in the box on the left?
In the box on the right draw as many squares as boats.

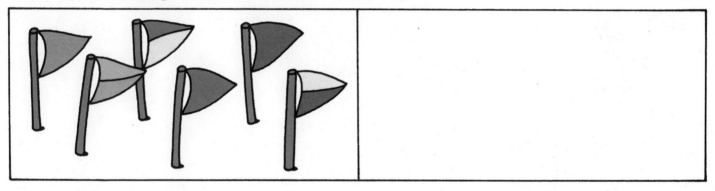

How many flags are there in the box on the left?
In the box on the right draw more circles than flags.

How many hearts are there in the box on the left?
In the box on the right draw fewer triangles than hearts.

Aim:
to sort objects into sets
with something in common.

Indoors and outdoors

Draw a circle round the objects used out of doors.
Tick the objects used indoors.

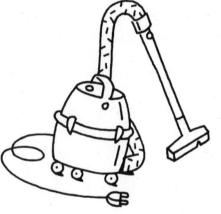

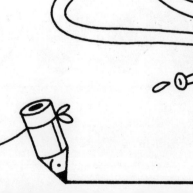

Flowers

In each column below, count the number of petals on the flowers on the left and draw the same number of petals on the stalks on the right.

On the river

How many boats have gone under the bridge already?
How many have yet to go under it?
How many boats are there altogether?

Mummy, may I have a dog, please?

All these children want a pet dog.
See if there are enough dogs for each child to have a pet by drawing one line from each child to a dog.

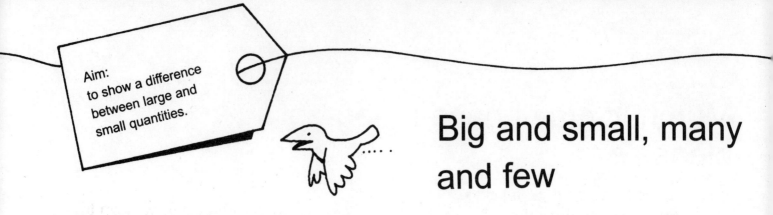

Big and small, many and few

Draw many small birds above the big house and draw just a few big birds over the small house.

Adding 2 more

Draw 2 more of the same object at the side of each of the three sets of objects on this page.
How many of each object are there now on the page? Write the totals between the lines on the right.

_____

_____

_____

_____

_____

_____

Aim:
to sort objects into sets
with something in common
and count and total them.

The fisherman and the musician

Which of the objects on this page are connected with a musician and which with a fisherman?
How many objects does each have and how many objects are there altogether?

Long ears

Aim:
to count and add two given quantities.

How many rabbits have escaped from the hutch?
How many rabbits are still inside the hutch?
How many rabbits does Stephen have altogether?

Bigger than (>), smaller than (<) or equal to (=)

The open side of the sign should be on the side of the bigger quantity.
The pointed side of the sign should be on the side of the smaller quantity.
If the quantities are the same use the 'equal to' sign.
Now put the correct signs in the three empty boxes.

A snake

The snakes below already have some boxes drawn in and the first one has been finished with the correct number of dotted boxes. Draw as many squares on the rest as are needed to make up the number on each snake's head.

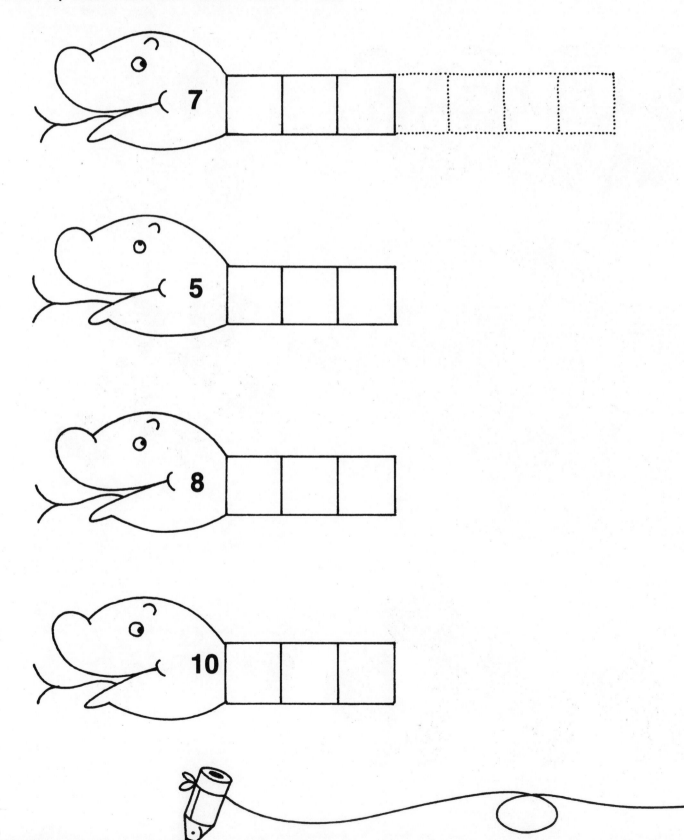

Aim:
to compare quantities in two sets and make the two sets equal.

Check the three pairs of drawings to see if there is a banana for each monkey, a fish for each dolphin and a bone for each dog. If there are not enough, draw the right number of each so that every animal can have one thing to eat.

Chickens and bottles

How many white chickens can you count and how many yellow chickens can you count?
Colour the white chickens in yellow. How many yellow chickens are there now?

How many full bottles can you count? How many empty bottles can you count?
Colour in the empty bottles. How many full bottles are there now?

Fruit

Count the pieces of fruit and put your answers on the
dotted lines.

 **+**    **3 + 4 = 7**

   **2 + 1 = ...**

   **1 + 4 = ...**

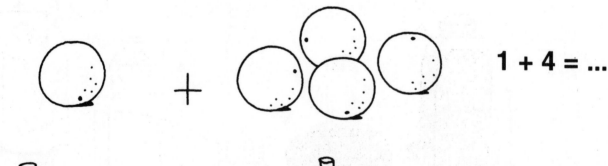   **4 + 4 = ...**

Make the pictures match the numbers

Aim:
to add or remove objects shown to arrive at a required quantity.

Count the objects in each set and check to see if they are the same as the figure shown for the set.

Then either put a line through an extra object or draw in the right number of missing objects, so everything matches.

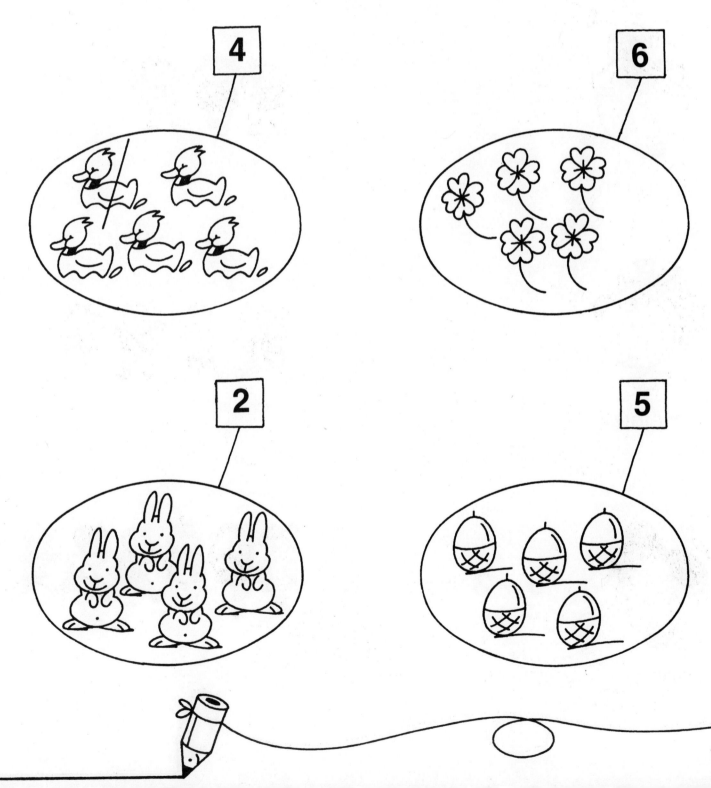

Brothers and sisters

How many brothers and sisters do Stephen, Helen and John have?
Do the sum, writing your answer on the dotted line, and then check it with the help of the drawings on the right.

2 + 1 = ...

Stephen

1 + 3 = ...

Helen

3 + 3 = ...

John

Counting and adding

Aim: to count and add together two sets of the same objects.

Write the number of the objects under each set and then add the two numbers together to make the total for each object.

A hot-air balloon

Do the sums in the balloon and write each answer in.
Then colour the sections of the balloon, according to your answers, as follows:-
green for 4, blue for 5, yellow for 6 and red for 9.

Triangles, squares and circles

Aim: to add given quantities and write the answers.

Count the shapes and write how many there are under each group, add the two numbers up and write the answers on the dotted lines.

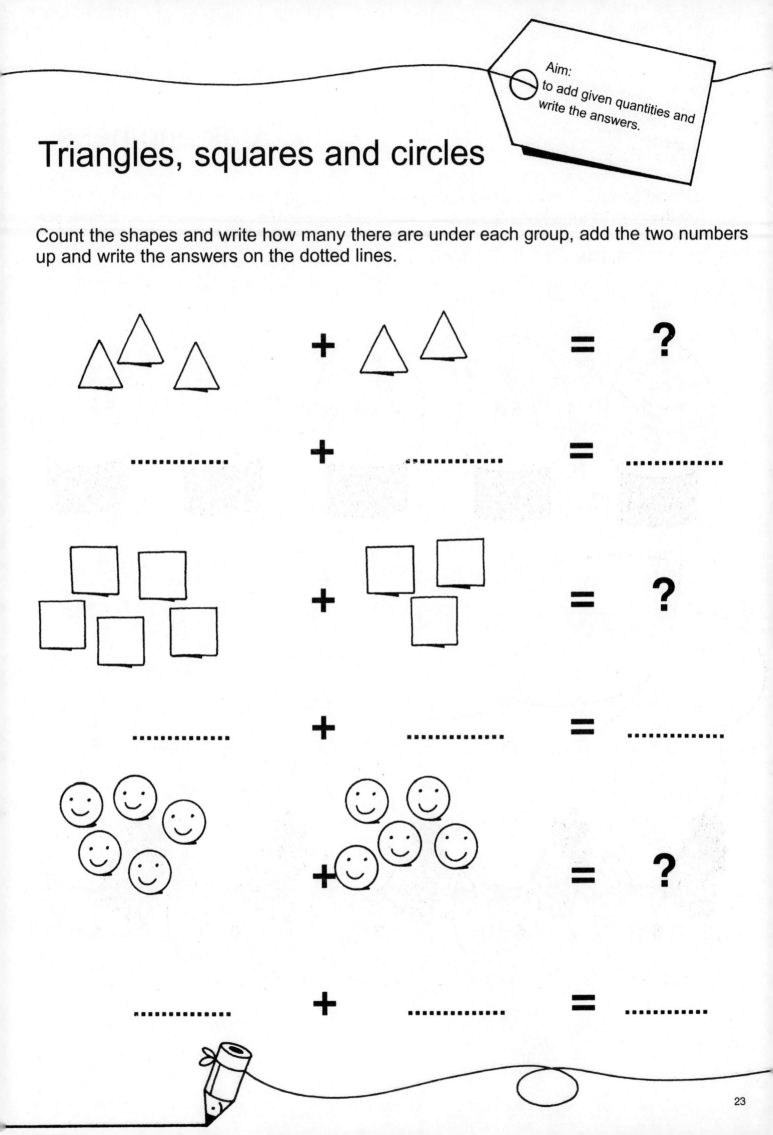

.... + ... = ...

.... + ... = ...

.... + ... = ...

23

Aim:
to do additions and match
the answers to numbers
between 1 and 10.

Eggs and hens

Do the sums in the eggs and then draw a line to the hen with the right answer, as in the example.

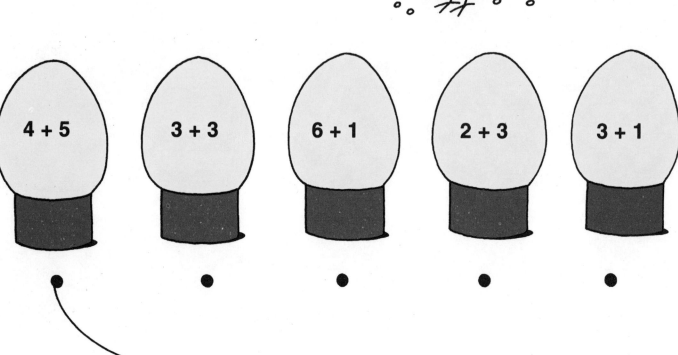

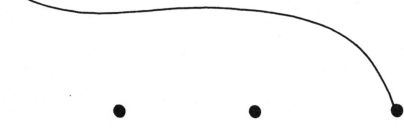

More or fewer

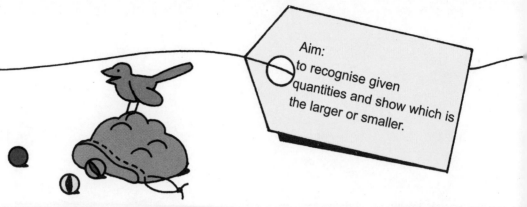

Aim: to recognise given quantities and show which is the larger or smaller.

Count the balls in the columns and write the number under each column. Then put in the correct sign for which is the larger or the smaller quantity.
(The open side of the sign should be on the side of the larger quantity.
The pointed side of the sign should be on the side of the smaller quantity.)

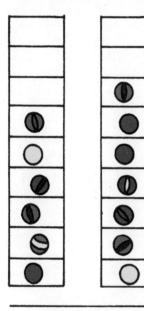

6 < 7

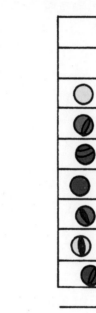

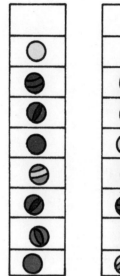

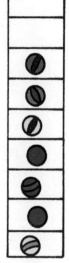

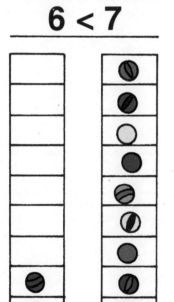

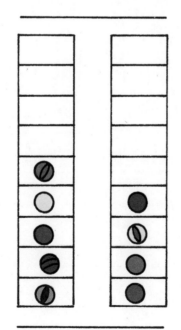

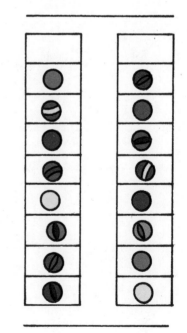

Aim:
to add to a given number
to reach a required number.

Setting the table

It is David's birthday. He is having a party and will need 8 forks, 8 knives and 8 spoons.
Draw the missing cutlery to show 8 of each sort.
Then write in the missing numbers to complete the sums.

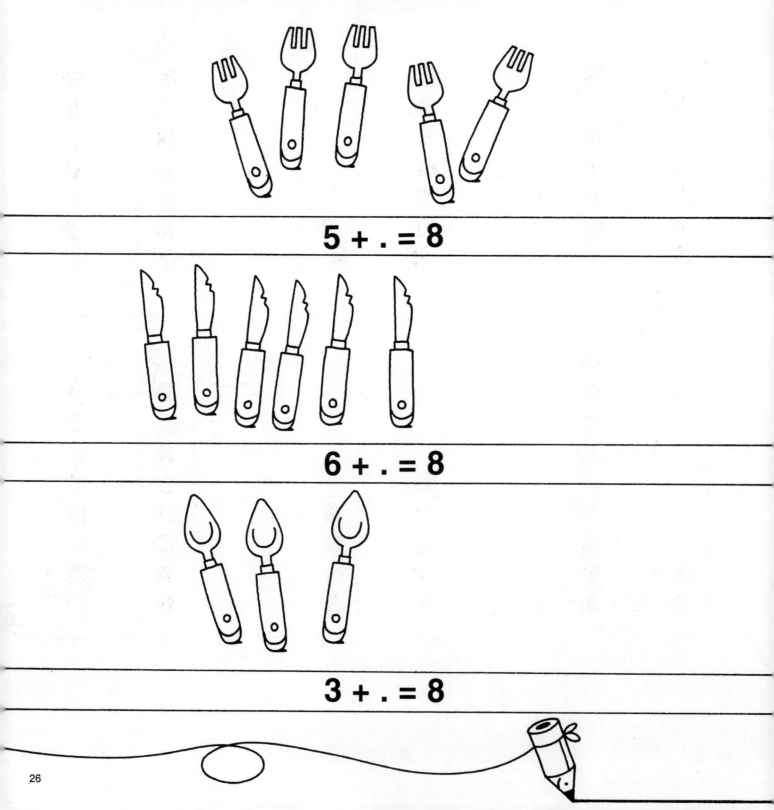

$5 + . = 8$

$6 + . = 8$

$3 + . = 8$

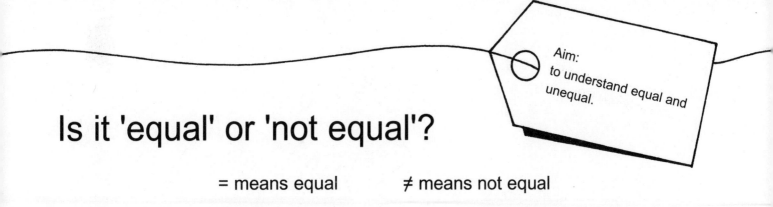

Is it 'equal' or 'not equal'?

= means equal   ≠ means not equal

There are three rows of objects on this page. Count how many are in each separate group and write the answers between the lines.
If there is the same number of objects on the left as on the right, put the = sign in the box in the middle.
If the numbers on the right and left are different put the ≠ sign in the box in the middle.

Just a few

Colour 8 of the fish in red.

Draw a circle round 4 of the balls.

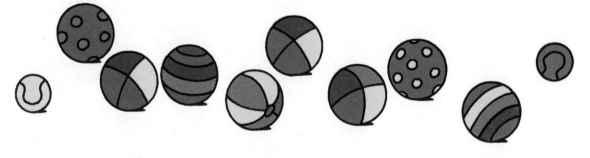

Put a tick by 6 of the hats.

Draw 3 more flowers. How many flowers are there altogether now?

Goal!

Aim:
to do additions and match the answers to pictures.

Do the sums and write in the answers. Then count the balls in the nets and draw a line to match each of the friends with the right number of goals.

6+2=

9+1=

1+5=

3+2=

29

The same result

Complete these sums so that, in each of the five pictures, your sums have an answer that is the same as the big number.

8

3 + ...

6 + ...

4 + ...

9

7 + ...

4 + ...

8 + ...

6

2 + ...

1 + ...

... + 3

0 + ...

7

2 + ...

4 + ...

1 + ...

5 + ...

2 + ...

4 + ...

3 + ...

1 + ...

5

Join the dots

Aim:
to follow the numbers
1 to 10 in sequence.

Do the sums and write in the answers. Then join the dots in order from 1 to 10 to show Helen the way back to her mother.

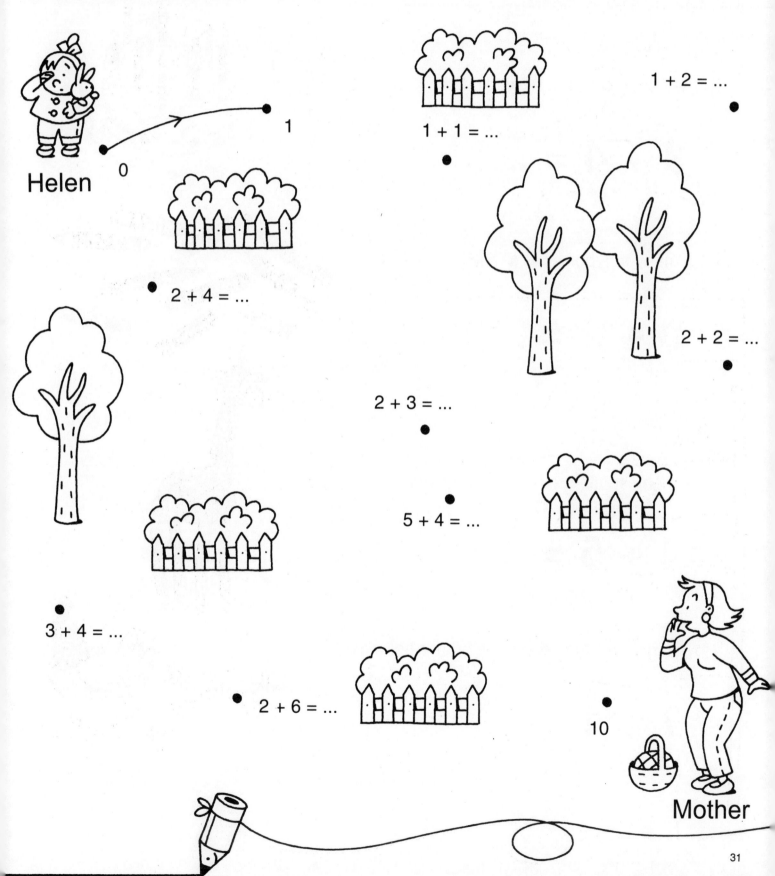

Helen
0
1

1 + 1 = ...

1 + 2 = ...

2 + 4 = ...

2 + 2 = ...

2 + 3 = ...

5 + 4 = ...

3 + 4 = ...

2 + 6 = ...

10

Mother

31

Aim:
to add numbers from 1 to 10
and check the answers by
looking at the pictures.

Look! I can count

Do the sums below and write the answers on the dotted lines.
Then check your answers by counting the objects in the pictures at the side.

It is Gerard's birthday. How old is he?

3 + 4 = ...

How many crayons does Michael have?

8 + 2 = ...

How many spots does this giraffe have?

4 + 5 = ...

How many chickens does the mother hen have?

7 + 1 = ...

LET'S COUNT

Clowns

The clown on the left has a few circles on his costume.
Draw a lot of circles on the costume of the clown on the right.

What goes with what?

Aim:
to identify a link
between two objects.

Draw a line with an arrow to join two objects which go together, as shown in the example.

The red butterfly

Scotty wants to catch a red butterfly. Draw a circle round the red butterfly.
Then write a full row of the number 1 between the lines at the bottom, using the dotted
lines and the arrows to help you.

From the smallest to the largest

Join the objects in each box with a line and an arrow, starting with the smallest and finishing with the largest, as shown in the example.

7 9 5 1

2 cherries

Join each pair of cherries together by drawing in the stalks, as shown in the examples. Then write a full row of the number 2 between the lines at the bottom, using the dotted lines and the arrows to help you.

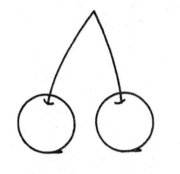

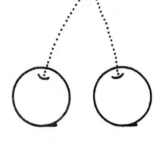

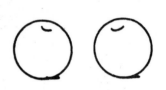

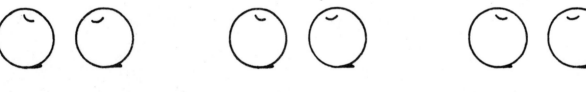

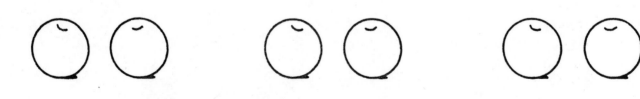

Big and little, in front of and behind

Aim:
to understand the differences between big and little, in front of and behind.

One pixie is hiding from his friend: see if you can draw his hat as he peeps out from behind the tree.
Draw a flower in front of the tree.
Draw a big mushroom next to the little mushroom.

Aim:
to identify objects
by size.

Find the bigger animal

Here are three pairs of animals.
Draw a circle round the bigger of each pair.

3 Indians

Aim:
to understand the meaning
of the number 3 and to
learn to write it correctly.

Here are 3 Indians jumping over a fence at the same time. Colour the first horse brown.
Then write a full row of the number 3 between the lines at the bottom, using the dotted
lines and the arrows to help you.

Which is the smaller?

There are several pairs of objects drawn below.
Colour the smaller of each pair in your favourite colours.

   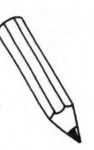 

Thick and thin

Draw a circle round each of the thick crayons and then colour all the crayons in your favourite colours.

43

Count the shells on the beach

There are several shells on the beach. Put a circle round each of the 4 grey ones.
Then write a full row of the number 4 between the lines at the bottom, using the dotted
lines and the arrows to help you.

Are there enough ice-creams?

Aim: to understand the meaning of the number 5 and to learn to write it correctly.

Here are 5 ice-creams in a row. To find out if there are enough for the children in the row below, draw a line from each child to an ice-cream.
Then write a full row of the number 5 between the lines at the bottom, using the dotted lines and arrows to help you.

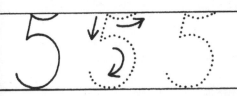

45

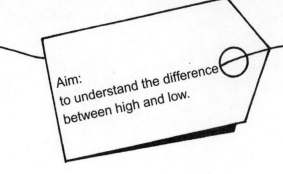

Aim:
to understand the difference
between high and low.

High and low

In each of the drawings below colour whoever is high in yellow and whoever is low in red.

By the river

Draw two more sheep on the left of the river and draw one more rabbit on the right of the river.

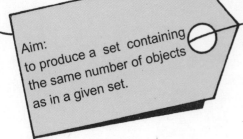

Aim:
to produce a set containing
the same number of objects
as in a given set.

In each of the three boxes on the right draw as many crosses as there are objects shown on the left. Then write the three correct numbers in the lines below the boxes, using the dotted lines to help you.

Find the 6 changes

The bottom picture is not quite the same as the top picture. See if you can find the 6 things which are different and draw a circle round each one.

Then write a full row of the number 6 between the lines at the bottom, using the dotted lines and the arrows to help you.

Aim:
to count with the numbers
2 and 4 and to associate
them with a given colour.

Brown and yellow creatures

Colour the creatures which are standing on 4 legs in yellow and colour the creatures on 2 legs in brown.

Colour by numbers

Aim:
to recognise numbers from 1 to 5 and to associate them with given colours.

Colour this drawing as follows: fill in all the sections marked 1 in blue, those marked 2 in yellow, those marked 3 in red, those marked 4 in orange and those marked 5 in green.

Balloons

Draw a circle round the child carrying the larger number of balloons.
Then add 2 more balloons to the smaller bunch.

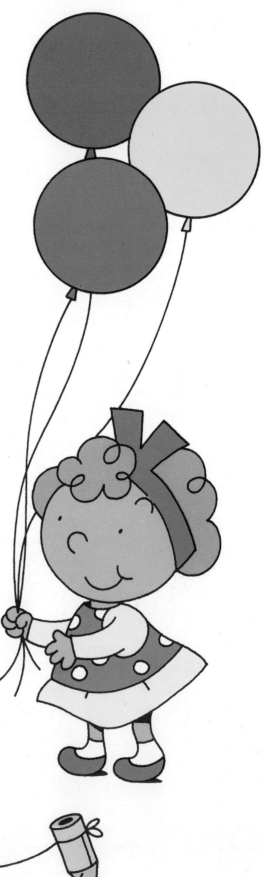

Multi-coloured hats

Aim:
to write a series of numbers correctly and to link them to drawings as required.

Give these chefs a number each in order from 1 to 5 and write the numbers in the lines below the drawing.
Then colour the hat of chef number 1 in yellow, the hat of chef number 3 in red and the hat of chef number 5 in blue.

1

4

A ladybird

This ladybird has 7 spots on her left wing. Draw 7 spots on her other wing to match.
Then write a full row of the number 7 between the lines at the bottom, using the dotted
lines and arrows to help you.

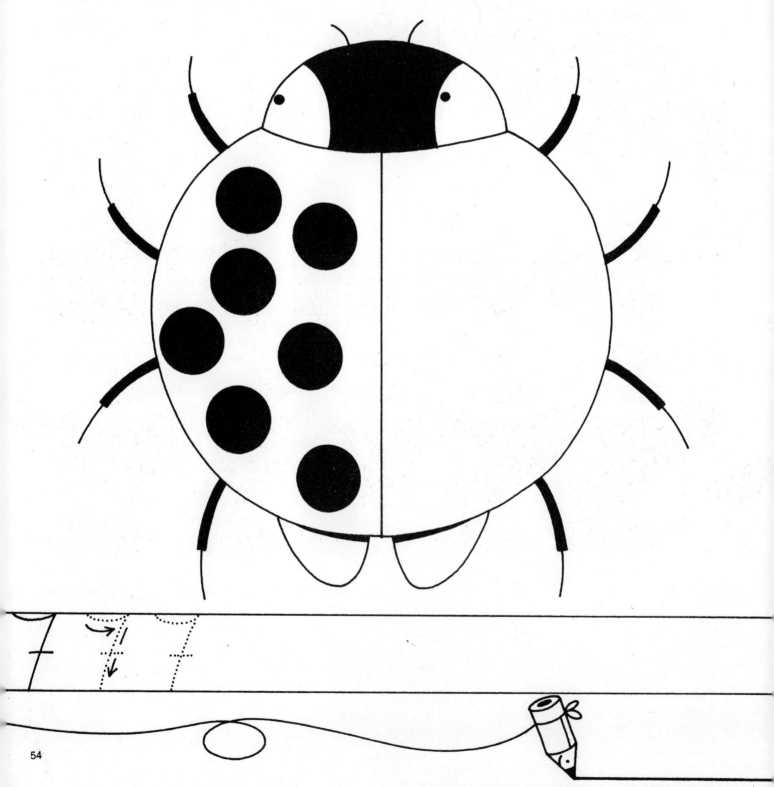

Two classrooms

Aim:
to understand the difference between large and small quantities.

One of these two classrooms has a larger number of children in it.
Decide which one it is and colour that picture.

Aim:
to understand the meaning
of the number 8 and to learn
to write it correctly.

Happy monkeys

How many of the monkeys have red hats?
Draw a circle round each monkey with a red hat.

Then write a full row of the number 8 between the lines
at the bottom, using the dotted lines and arrows to
help you.

Count and compare

Aim:
to distinguish between different quantities of the same object.

There are four kinds of objects on this page. Draw a circle round the set in each pair which contains the fewer objects.

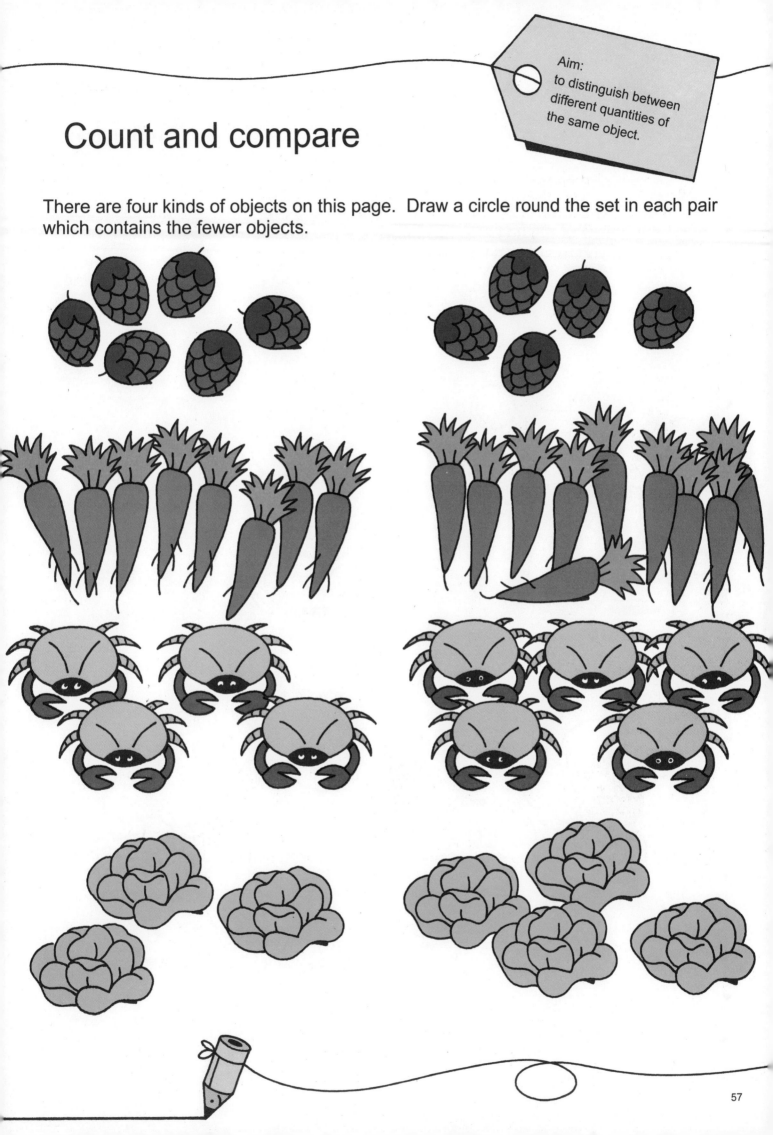

Aim:
to distinguish different
and identical quantities
of the same object.

Draw a green line between the two children who have blown the same number of bubbles. Colour the trousers of the boy who has blown the most bubbles in blue. Colour the trousers of the boy who has blown the fewest bubbles in red.

Count and colour

Aim: to identify quantities from 1 to 10.

Draw a circle round the set of 3 objects and a circle round the set of 7 objects.
Then colour all the drawings on the page.

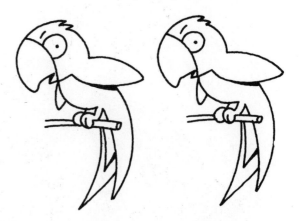

Aim:
to understand the meaning
of the number 9 and to learn
to write it correctly.

Red and green apples

Not all the apples on this tree are ripe. How many ripe, rosy red ones can you count?
Then write a full row of the number 9 between the lines at the bottom, using the dotted
lines and the arrows to help you.

10 fingers

Aim:
to understand the meaning of the number 10 and to learn to write it correctly.

Look, Mummy! Now I can count to 10!

Write a full row of the number 10 between the lines at the bottom, using the dotted lines and the arrows to help you.

10 10 10

Colour the larger quantity

There are five different kinds of objects on this page. In each pair, colour the set which contains the larger number of objects.

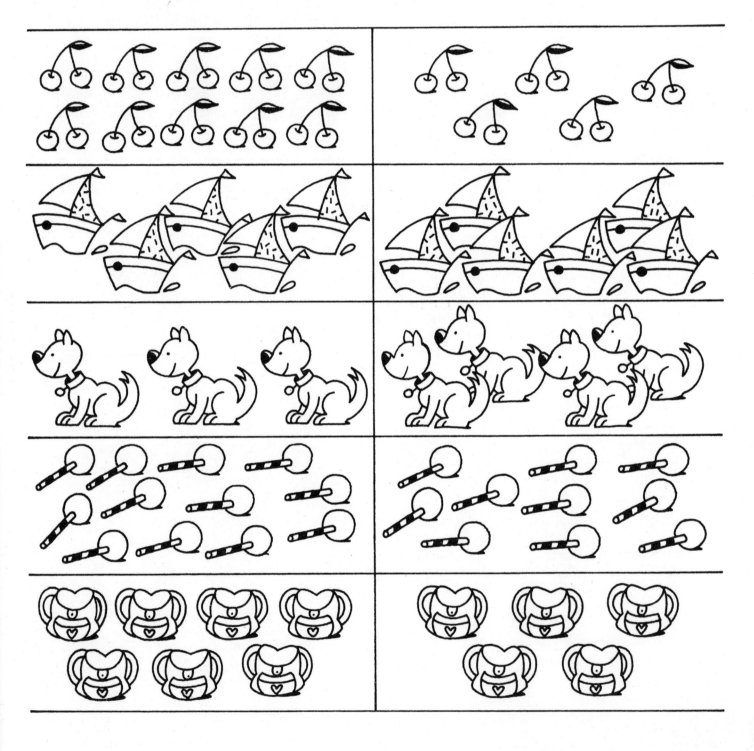

In a little station

Aim:
to write the numbers 1 to 10 in the correct order.

How about a train ride?
Write the missing numbers on the carriages.

1

3

4

7

Aim:
to practise the
numbers from 1 to 10.

Join the numbers from 1 to 10

In the two pictures below, first join the numbers 1 to 10 with the dots and then join the numbers 1 to 10 with the squares.

LET'S WRITE

Centre, left and right

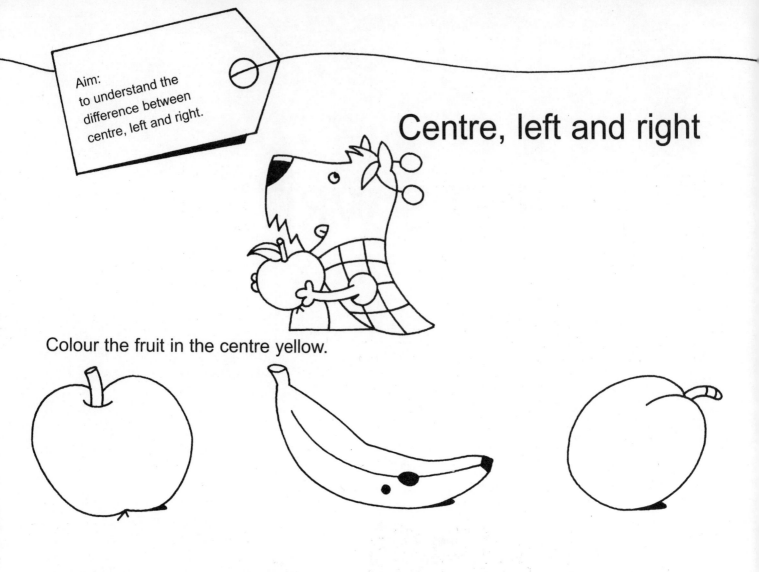

Colour the fruit in the centre yellow.

Colour the fruit on the left red.

Colour the fruit on the right green.

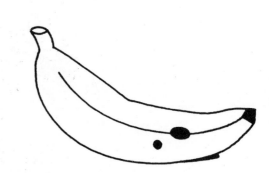

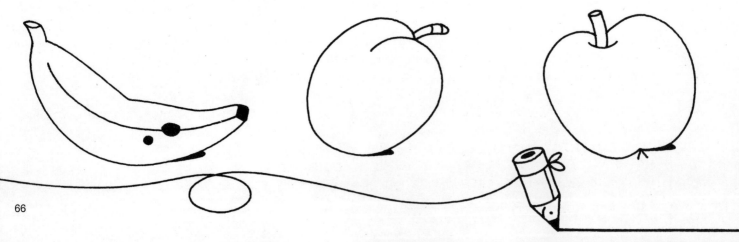

Under the shower

Scotty is taking a refreshing shower.
Join the little dots to make the water look really wet!

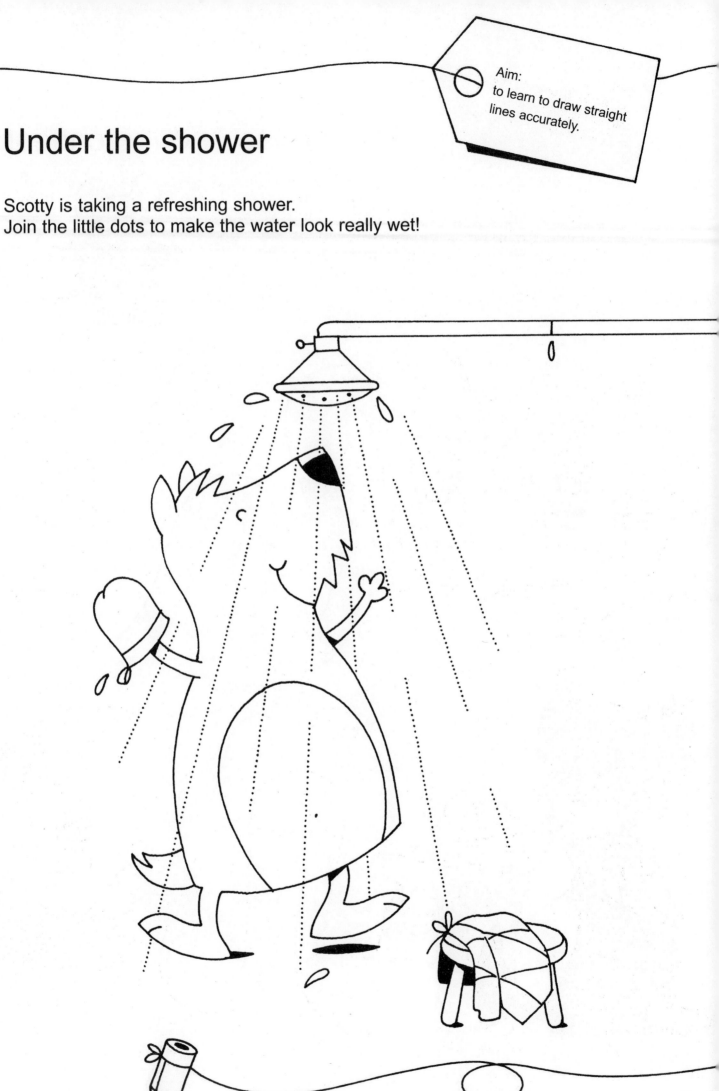

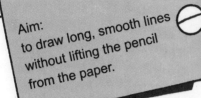
The mouse and the cheese

This mouse is hungry and wants a piece of that cheese. Show him the way to the cheese by drawing a line along the path without lifting the pencil from the paper.

Find the five changes

Aim:
to improve observation
of small differences.

The bottom picture is not quite the same as the top picture. See if you can find the five things which make it different and draw a circle around each one.

A fine day by the sea

The sun is shining but it is breezy so there are some waves on the sea.
Join the dots to show the waves, using the arrows to help you.

70

Find the odd-man-out

Aim:
to improve observation
of small differences.

One of these sheep is different from all the others.
Colour him in a dark colour.

Aim:
to identify objects which
do not belong in a set.

Find the odd-man-out

There are three sets of objects on this page.
Put a circle round each object which does not belong in its set.

Not quite the same!

There are six sets of drawings on this page of two almost identical objects. Each two should be the same but one tiny difference has crept in and something is missing. Look carefully and put a circle round each mistake.

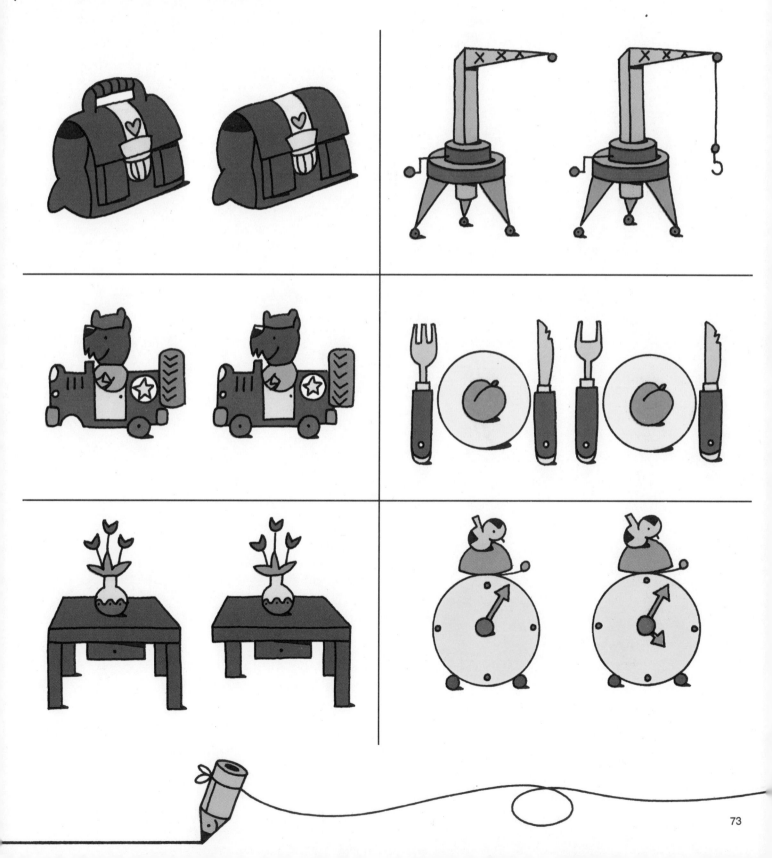

Aim:
to learn how to write
the letter 'c' and
similar letters.

Under the water

Some of the scales on these fish are missing.
Draw them in by following the dotted lines.

Skittles

Aim:
to recognise individual,
isolated letters.

There are some skittles on this page.
Colour the parts marked 'a' in yellow. Colour the parts marked 'b' in blue. Colour the parts marked 'c' in red.
Then give all the skittles coloured hats.

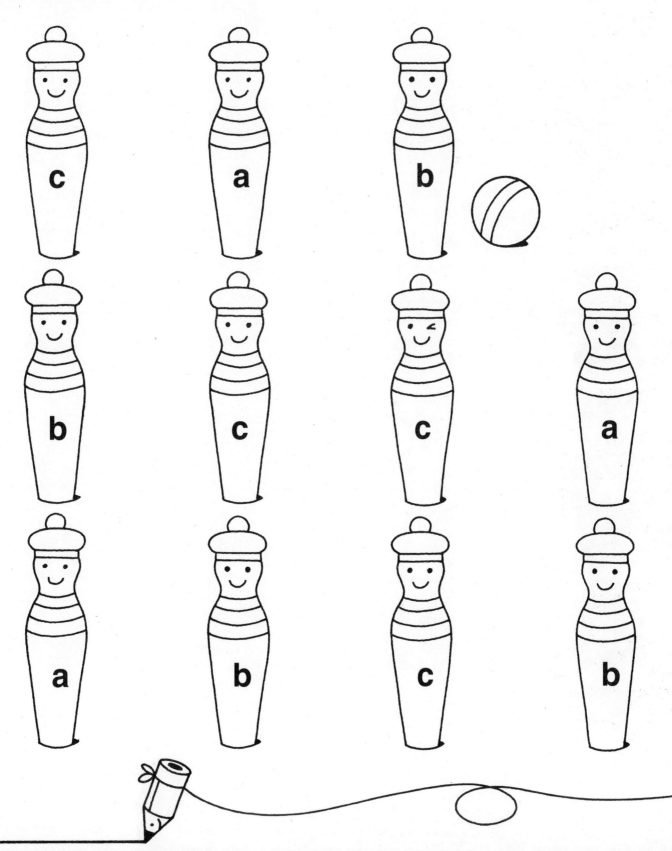

Racing cars

These racing cars are ready to go.

Draw the smoke coming out of their exhaust-pipes, using the dotted lines and the arrows to help you.

Complete each pattern without taking the pencil from the paper.

The first one is done for you.

A clever clown

Aim: to recognise that letters make a word.

Draw a line from each letter of the big, black word 'clown' to the same letter written on one of the balls the clown is juggling. The lines can cross over each other.

C L O W N

A little train

Draw over the dotted lines of the squares, rectangles and triangles. Finish each shape in one go without taking the pencil from the paper.

Then finish the drawing of the little train at the bottom of the page.

Grandma's cat

Aim:
to practise a writing pattern for the 'tailed' letters, 'f', 'j', 'g' and 'y'.

Look! The kitten is playing with Grandma's knitting wool.
Draw the wool, using the dotted lines and the arrows to help you.

Aim:
to practise writing upper
and lower loops.

Will you skip with us?

All the children on this page are skipping but some of the ropes are missing.
Draw in the ropes, using the dotted lines and the arrows to help you.

Find the right shadow

Aim: to pick out one particular shape from several shapes.

The snail at the top has found his shadow.
Find the shadow which matches the objects drawn on the left.

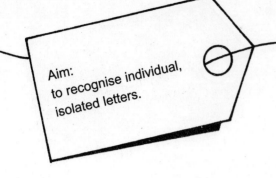
Hot-air balloons

There are a lot of hot-air balloons on this page.
Colour all the ones marked with the letter 'o' in blue. Colour all the ones marked with the
letter 'm' in yellow. Colour all the ones marked with the letter 'n' in red.

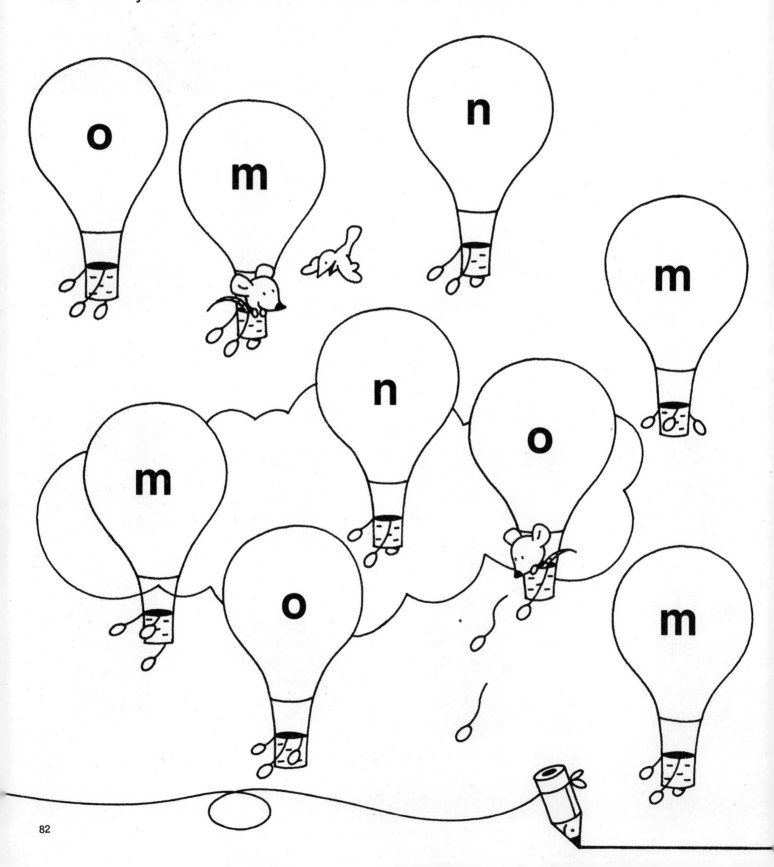

Glasses on noses

Aim:
to learn to write the letter 'o' correctly.

Join the dots in the direction of the arrows, starting at the big, black dot at the top of each circle.

Then make sure that all six children at the bottom of the page have proper glasses.

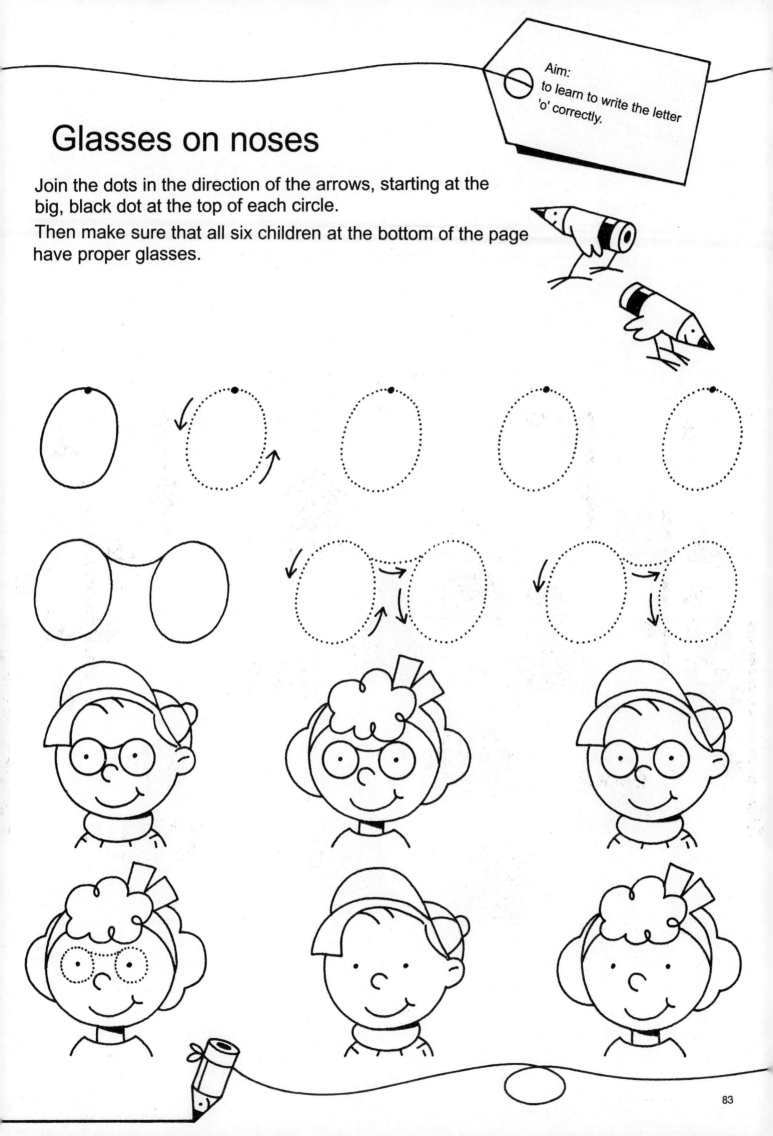

83

On your marks . . . Get set . . . Go!

Look for the kart with the letter 'o' and put a circle round it.

Then write a full row of the letter 'o' between the lines at the bottom, using the dotted lines and the arrows to help you.

Half a butterfly

Aim:
to observe carefully and
copy an exact pattern.

Complete this drawing of a butterfly so that both wings are the same.

Apples

It is autumn and most of the apples on this tree are already ripe but some of the lines are missing so draw them in.

Then write a full row of the letter 'c' in the lines at the bottom, using the dotted lines and the arrows to help you.

Cluck, cluck, cluck . . . an egg!

Aim: to learn to draw both vertical and horizontal curved lines.

There is an egg-cup at the bottom of the page for each egg that Clara has laid but there are some lines missing so follow the dotted lines and finish the egg-cups.

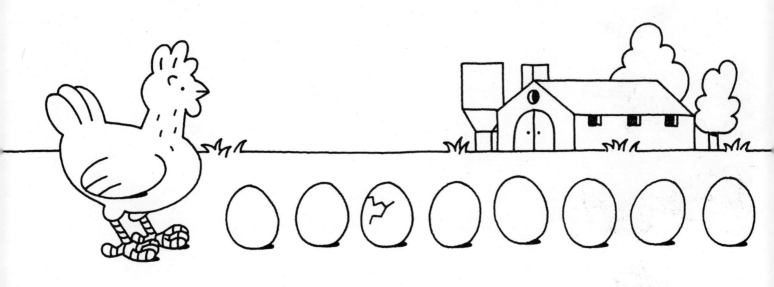

Aim:
to practise writing the
upper loops of letters.

A steamship

Draw the smoke coming out of the ships' funnels.

Then write a full row of loops in the lines at the bottom of the page, using the dotted lines and the arrows to help you.

Complete each pattern without taking the pencil from the paper.

Find the missing shape

Aim: to complete sets of shapes by comparison with a given set.

Look carefully at the set of shapes inside the circle.
Then look at each square and draw in the shape that is missing from the set.

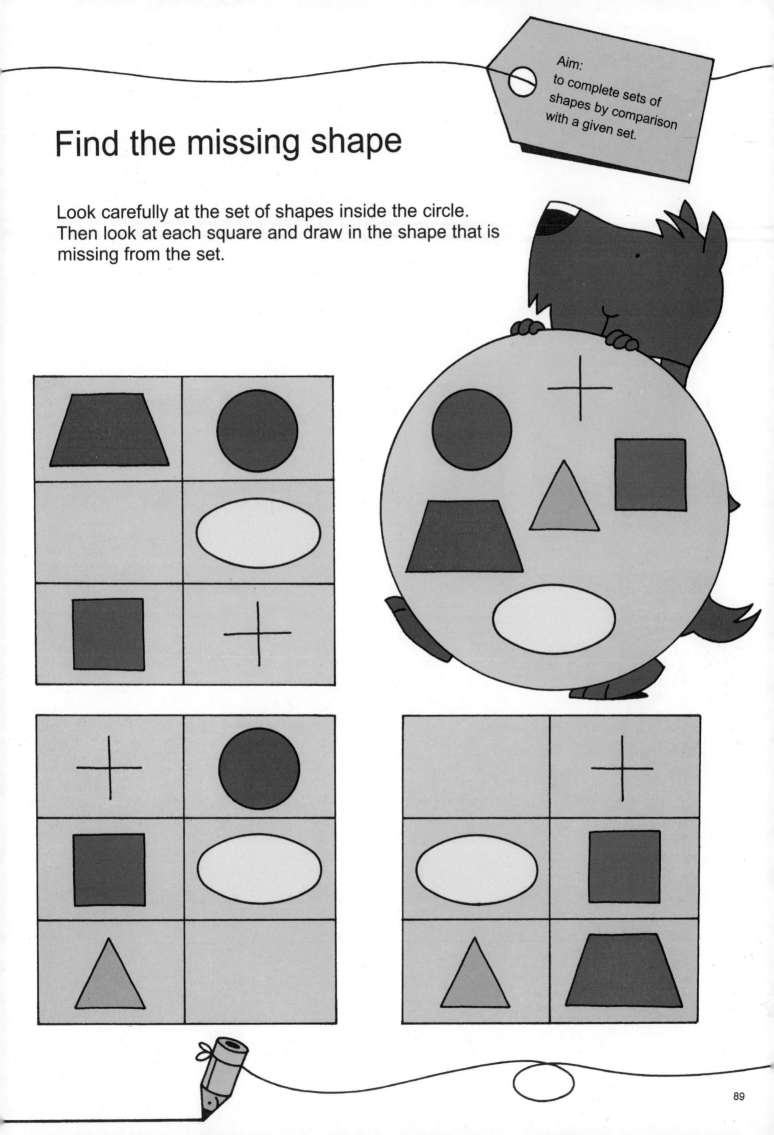

Umbrella or sunshade?

Complete these umbrellas and sunshades by drawing in their handles.
Then write a full row of the letter 't' in the lines at the bottom,
using the dotted lines and the arrows to help you.

90

Toadstools

Aim:
to learn to write the letter 'n' correctly.

Finish drawing the top of each toadstool.
Then draw a full row of the letter 'n' in the lines at the bottom,
using the dotted lines and the arrows to help you.

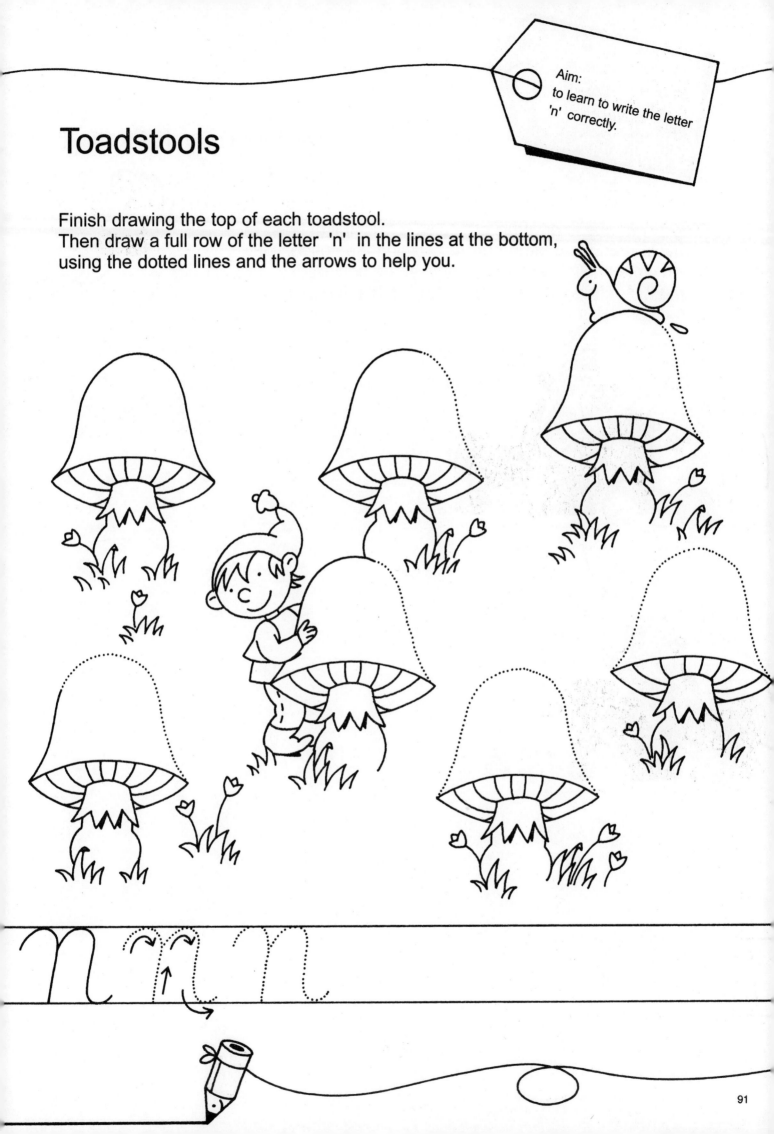

A bumpy journey

The clown has to drive his car down a road full of holes.
Draw the road and the holes by following the dotted lines.
Then write a full row of the letter 'u' at the bottom,
using the dotted lines and the arrows to help you.

Flowers

The wind has blown away some of the petals, centres and stalks from these flowers.
Draw along the dotted lines and complete the flowers.

Find the same word

Look at the word in the box on the left and then put a ring round the same word in the line of words on the right.

| bear | fear | ear | bear | tear |

| hen | den | pen | mend | hen |

| sea | sea | meal | meat | seal |

| dog | doll | dog | dot | dig |

The monkey and the coconuts

Aim:
to find differences between two drawings by careful observation.

Look carefully at the drawing on the left.
Then draw in what is missing from the picture on the right.

The letter 't'

Put a circle round all the words that have the letter 't' in them.

turtle

train

angel

witch

table

star

pear

dirty

watch

window

pitch

apple

LET'S FIND OUT

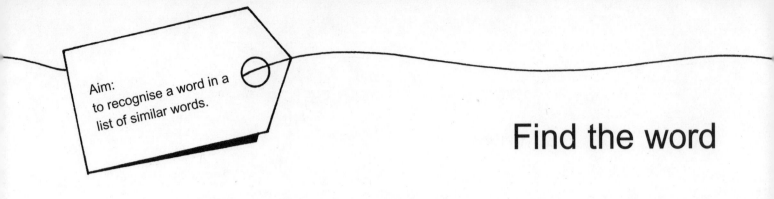

Aim:
to recognise a word in a
list of similar words.

Find the word

Look at each word in the box on the left. Find the same word in the list of words on the right and draw a circle round it.

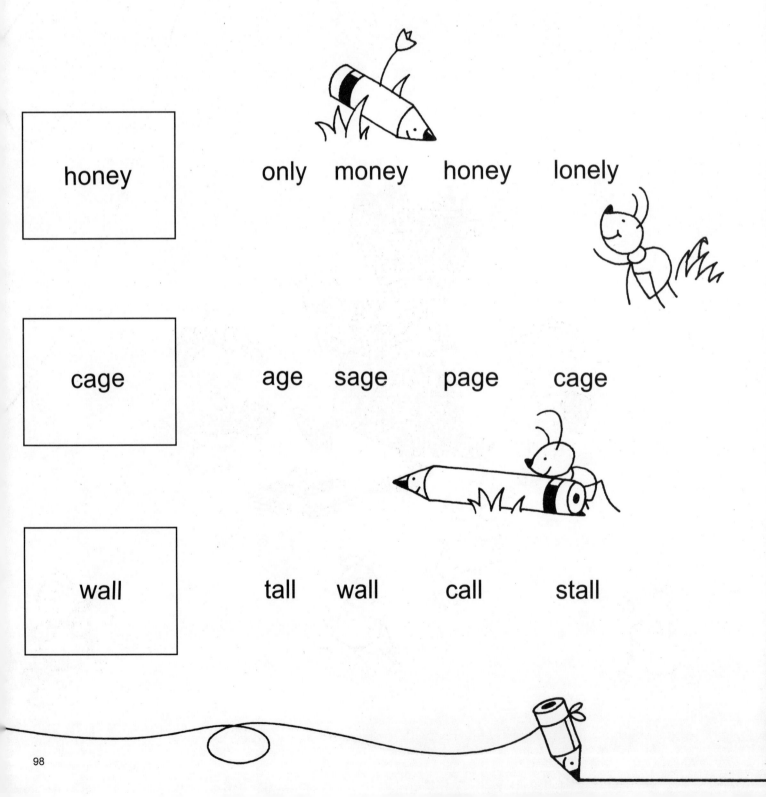

| honey | only   money   honey   lonely |

| cage | age   sage   page   cage |

| wall | tall   wall   call   stall |

Fun in the snow

Aim:
to follow a curved line.

These skiers are coming down the mountain at full speed.
Draw in their tracks by following the dotted lines.

Aim:
to add 1 to and subtract
1 from a given quantity.

Adding and subtracting 1

Count the objects in the middle boxes. Remember the answers.
In the boxes on the left put 1 more cross than there are objects in the middle.
In the boxes on the right put 1 cross fewer than there are objects in the middle.

Stephen's aquarium

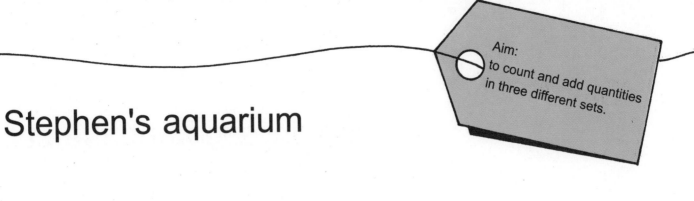

Aim: to count and add quantities in three different sets.

Stephen has an aquarium containing 5 red fish, 2 blue fish and 1 yellow fish. How many fish does Stephen have altogether?

The kangaroo and the ball

Will the kangaroo catch the ball?
Help him by drawing over the dotted lines.

Count and colour

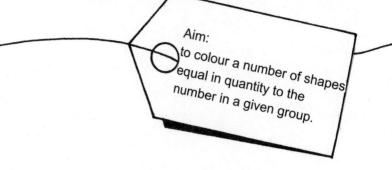
Aim:
to colour a number of shapes
equal in quantity to the
number in a given group.

Count the bicycles and then colour an equal number of circles in red.

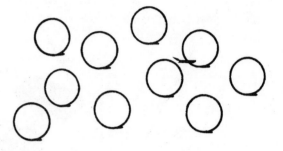

Count the teddy bears and then colour an equal number of squares in blue.

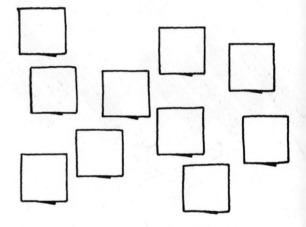

Count the ducks and then colour an equal number of triangles in green.

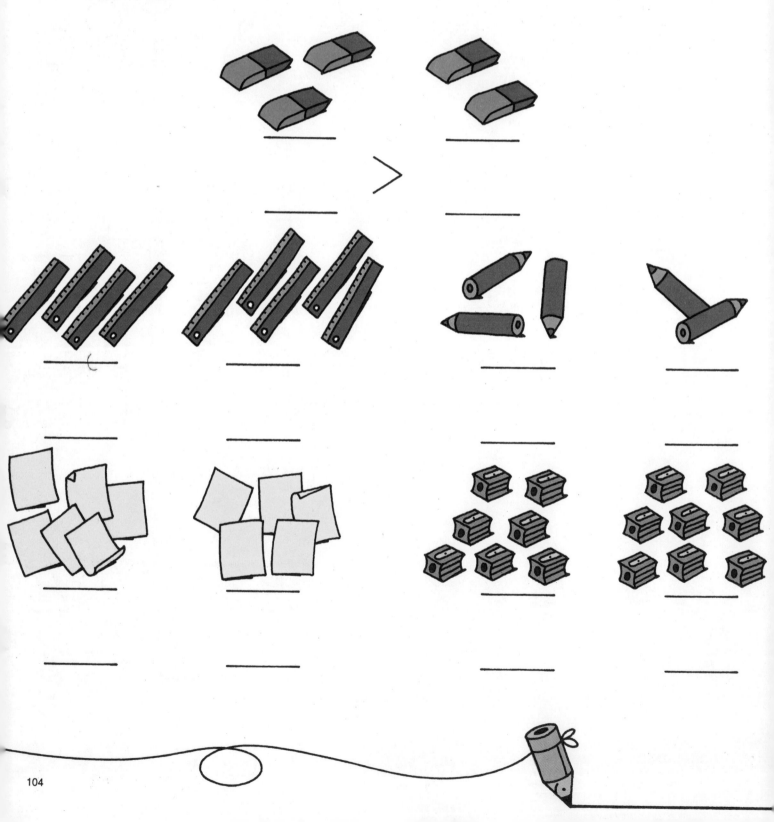

Count and compare

Count the objects in each group in the five sums below and write the answers in the lines under each group.

Then put the sign '>' (is greater than) or '<' (is smaller than) between each pair of numbers, as in the example.

Catch the ball!

Aim:
to draw curved lines.

Follow the direction of the ball in the air by filling in the dotted lines in the direction of the arrows.

Flying fish

Follow the dotted lines to draw the curves the fish make jumping in and out of the water. Then complete the ripples they make, without taking the pencil from the paper.

2 more

Count the objects on the left, add 2 to the answer and write the total number on the right.

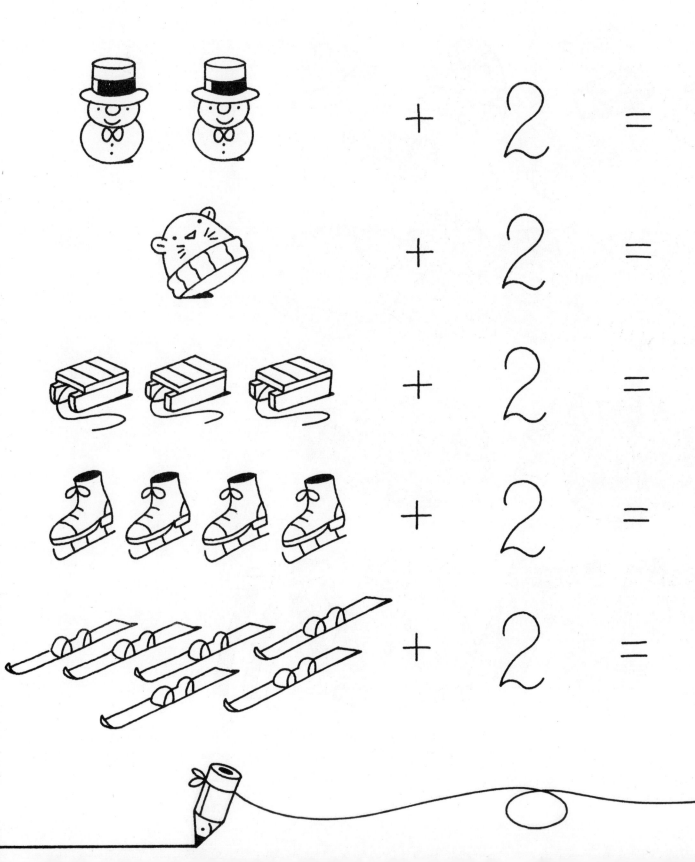

$+ \; 2 \; =$

$+ \; 2 \; =$

$+ \; 2 \; =$

$+ \; 2 \; =$

$+ \; 2 \; =$

Winter-time

It is starting to get cold and Mother counts all Lucy's and John's winter clothes.
Count the clothes in each set and write the answers in the spaces.

=

=

=

=

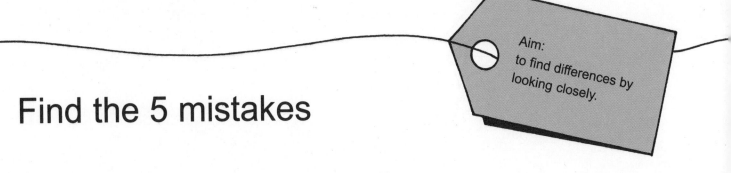

Find the 5 mistakes

The bottom picture is not quite the same as the top picture. Find the 5 things that are different and draw a circle round them.

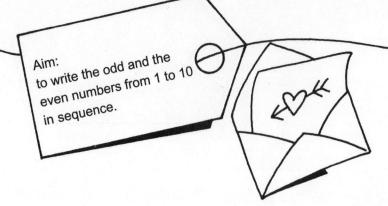

Odd and even

There are two rows of houses on this page. The top row has odd numbers and the bottom row has even numbers. Fill in the missing numbers in the right order.

Find the triangles

Aim:
to recognise triangles
among other shapes.

Colour in red all the triangles you can find on this page.

Aim:
to draw straight lines
and right angles.

Scotty, the dog

Show Scotty the path back to his kennel by following the dotted line without taking the pencil off the paper.

A race

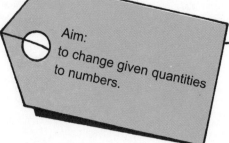

How many runners have not yet reached the finishing post?
How many have already passed it?
How many runners are there altogether?
Write your answers in the lines at the bottom.

___ + ___ = ___
___   ___   ___

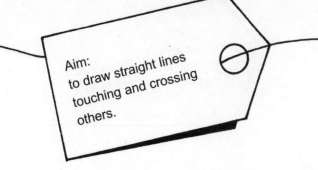

Aim:
to draw straight lines touching and crossing others.

Start at the arrows at the bottom and follow each line carefully to a house to find out where each child lives. Use a different colour for each child.

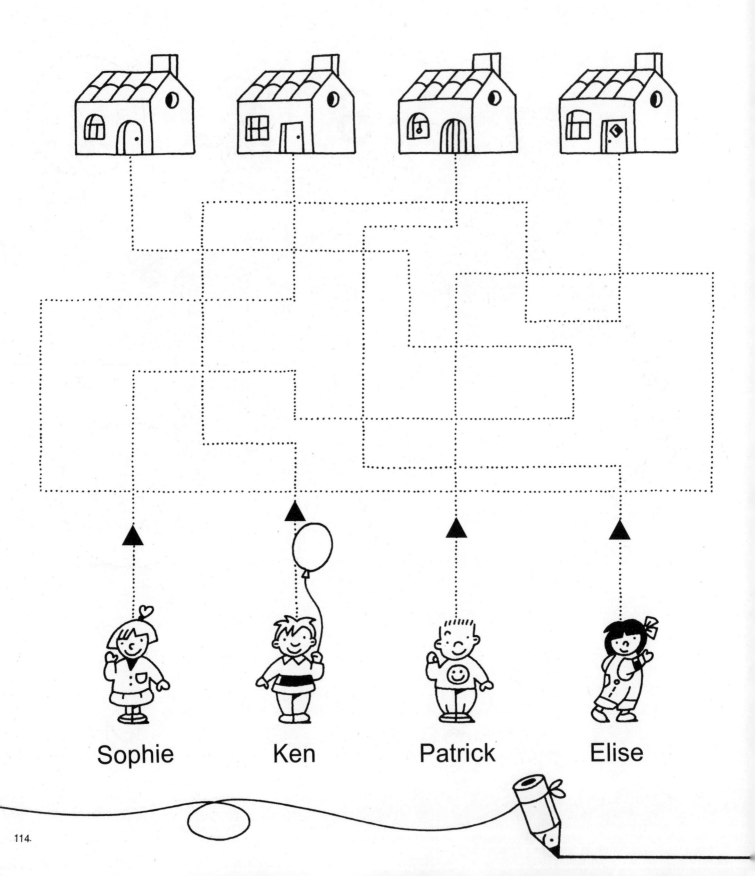

Sophie

Ken

Patrick

Elise

Which out of four?

Aim: to add two numbers and match the answer to a given number.

In the two pictures below, do all the sums and then put another circle round the sum with the answer that is the same as the number on the box.

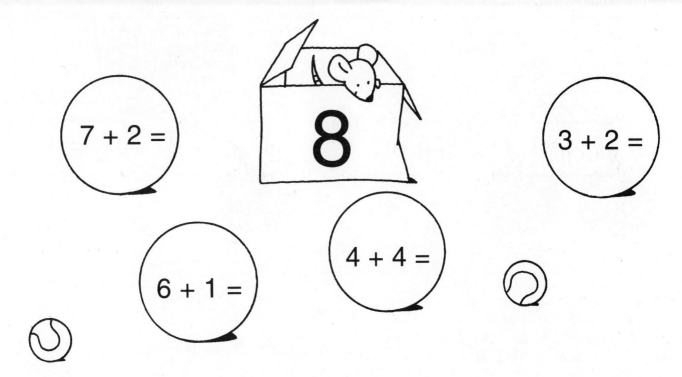

7 + 2 =

8

3 + 2 =

6 + 1 =

4 + 4 =

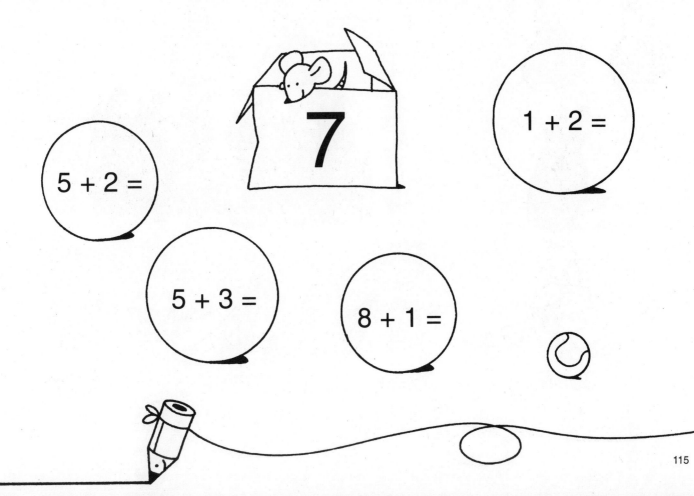

5 + 2 =

7

1 + 2 =

5 + 3 =

8 + 1 =

Count the fruit

Count the pieces of fruit, do the sums and write the answers after the =

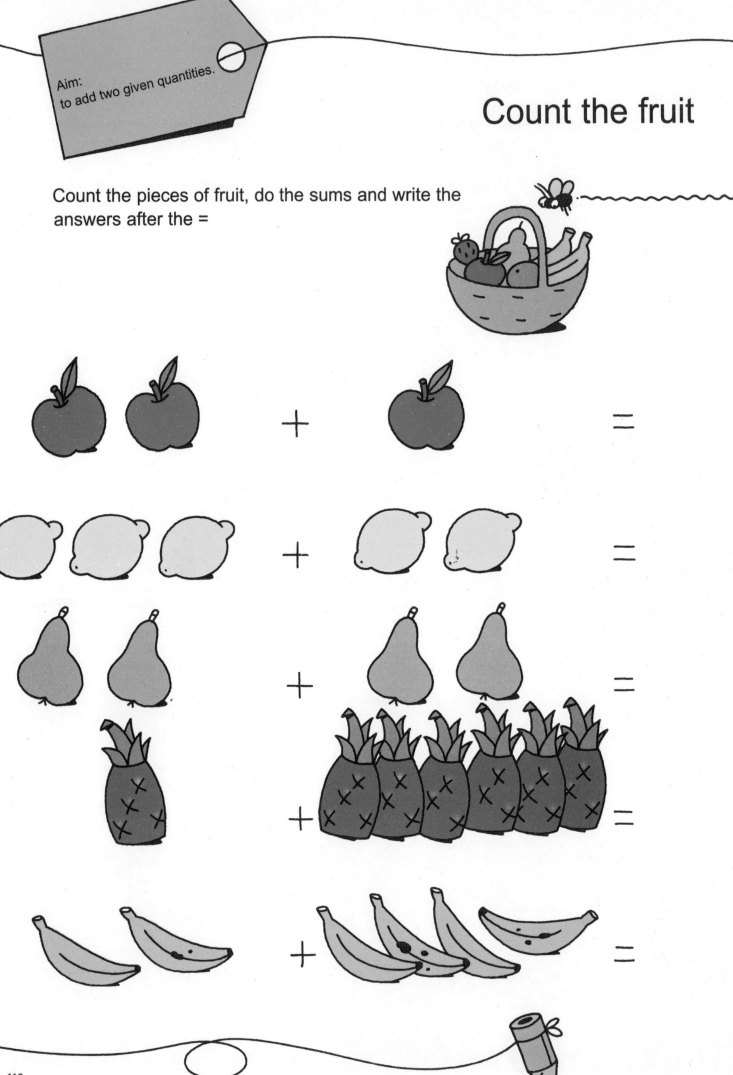

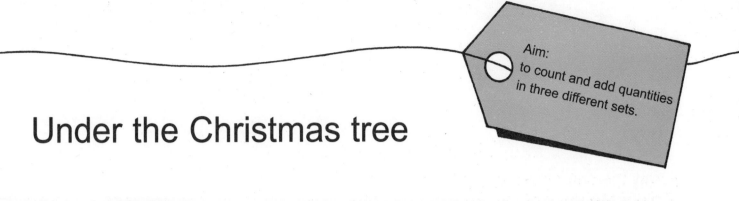

Under the Christmas tree

Aim:
to count and add quantities in three different sets.

Under the Christmas tree there are 3 blue parcels, 2 green parcels and 4 yellow parcels. How many parcels are there altogether?

Uncle Paul's house

Draw the sun above Uncle Paul's house.
Colour the trunk of the tree on the right.
Draw some curtains at the lower windows.
Colour the car on the left in red.

Long and short

In the picture below there are some paint brushes. Colour the long ones in red and the short ones in blue.

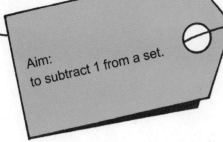

Aim:
to subtract 1 from a set.

In each set 1 object has been crossed out.
How many are left? Write the answer in the box on the right.

=

=

=

Complete with crosses

Aim:
to add to a given number to reach a required number.

In each of the three pairs below, count the objects ringed on the left.
Then, in the ring on the right, draw the number of crosses needed
to arrive at the number in the square.

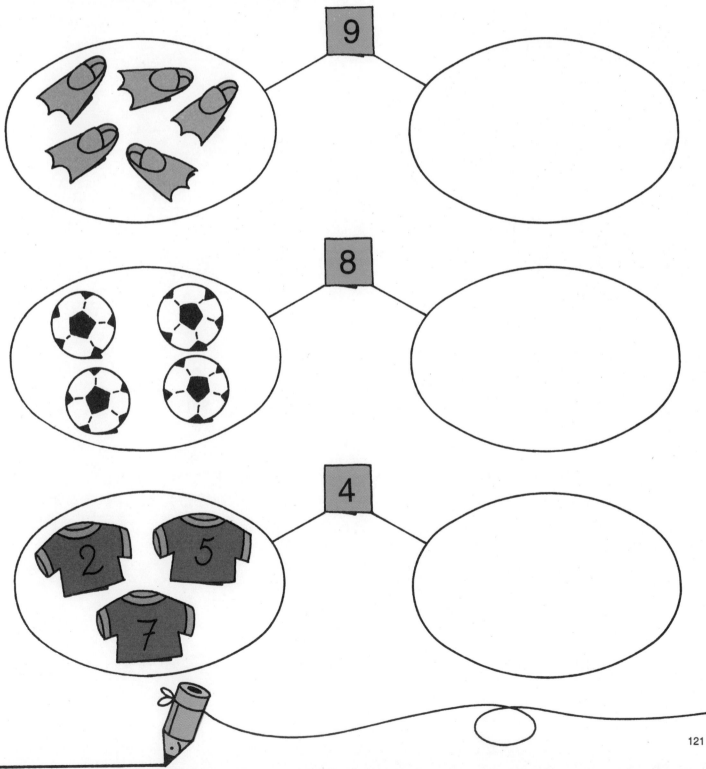

Aim:
to add sets of two numbers
and to match the answers
with a colour.

A hidden picture

Do all the sums in the circle and write your answers under each sum.
Then colour the sections according to your answers. If the answer is 5 use blue; if it is 7 use yellow; if it is 8 use red: if it is 10 use green.

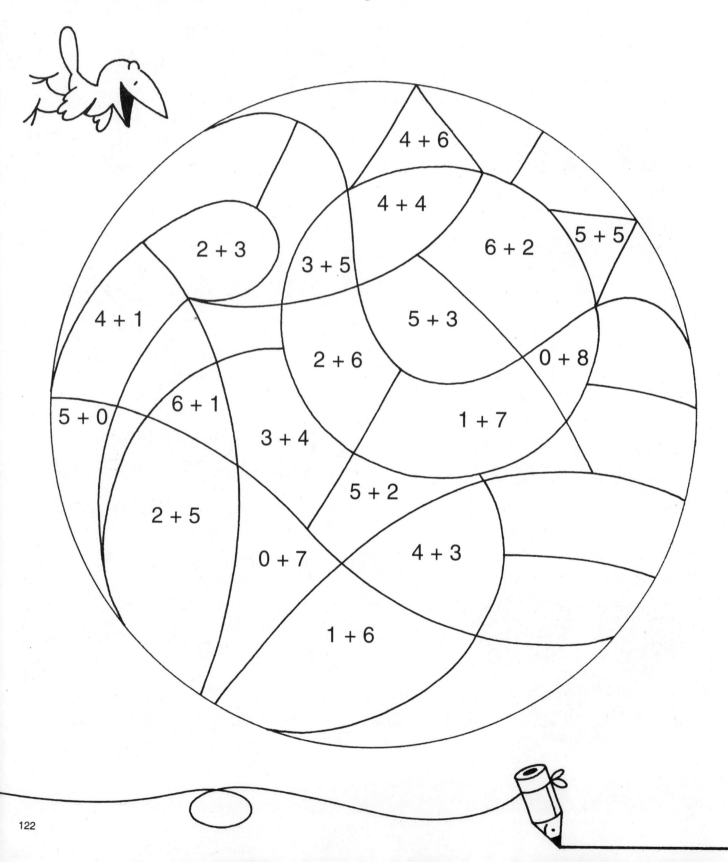

First and last

Colour the first creature in each line with your favourite colour and then put a circle round the last creature in each line.

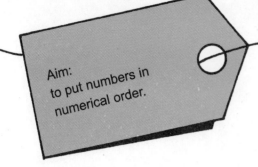

Aim:
to put numbers in numerical order.

Do the sums in the clouds.
Then starting with the smallest answer draw a line with an arrow to the next highest number and so on until you reach the biggest number.

1 + 2 =

2 + 2 =

2 + 5 =

2 + 0 =

4 + 1 =

5 + 5 =

Stephen and the bee

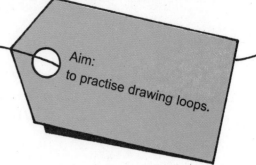
Buzzy the bee seems to want a taste of Stephen's ice cream. Follow the dotted lines with a pencil to see how she has been circling around his head.

At the zoo

Colour the big monkeys in brown and the small monkeys in yellow.
How many monkeys can you see altogether?

Find the linked objects

Aim:
to distinguish objects with
something in common.

Draw a circle round thing that can be used in a classroom.

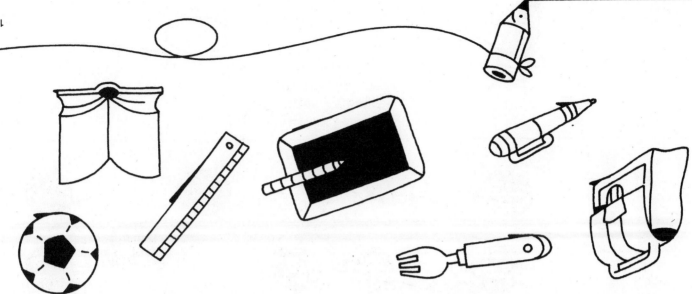

Draw a circle round each thing we can eat.

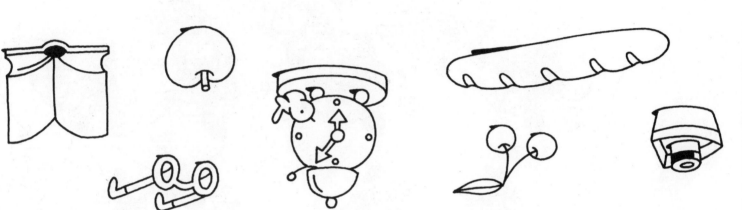

Draw a circle round each vegetable.

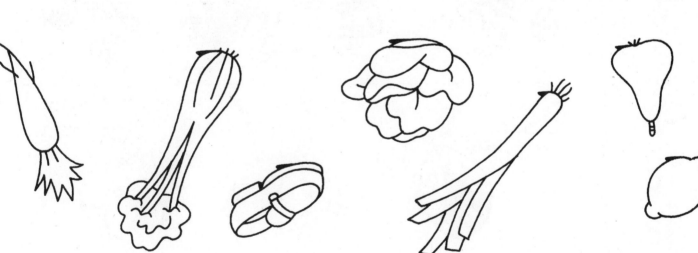

Published by Peter Haddock Ltd,
Bridlington England
© Caramel SA.
Printed in India.

Count the creatures

Count the creatures and put a circle round the correct answer in the column on the right.

	6 8 9
	8 7 6
	4 3 2
	4 3 2

Aim:
to count given
quantities.